I Will Live My Best Life Too

By Martika Shanel

Illustrated by
Maurice Terry Jr

Martika Shanel

The artist used traditional methods and Sketchbook Pro, scanned into Adobe Photoshop, to create the illustrations for this book. Disclaimer: The author is not, and does not engage in rendering psychological, or any other professional medical services--competent medical professionals shall be sought for such services.

For my everything, Penelope and Hugh, and all children affected by the opioid crisis — may your dreams be grand and realized.

- M.S.

● ● ○ ○

To Darius and Maurice Sr., my unbreakable warriors of strength, persistence, and a sure will to move beyond obstacles.

-M.T.

Mom,

This book is for you--to your former twenty-something-year-old self.

For the record, I always knew you could exceed your full potential.

Your Sunshine

I sometimes wonder, *Is this it?*
Can I have a future that's better
than this?

I love my parents. Yes, it's true. Although
I'm hurt by some things that they do, I
understand they make mistakes too.

Just as a rainbow comes after the rain, the sun will shine through my windowpane.

So I make note that my life will be fine--to press forward, do my best, and be kind.

That positivity, challenges, and an open mind will place me where I want to be in due time.

Although my life at home may be less than ideal, I can live out life's biggest thrills.

And if my life's the best one could receive, I'll still carve out time to envision my dreams.

Student Excellence
AWARD
SERVE | INSPIRE | LEAD

Student Achiever Award

SHIP

SPIRIT

Hard Worker

My effort put in is the effort received. A strong work ethic will help me achieve.

Attaining a dream is hard, indeed. But a bit of grit and a dash of ambition will help supply the tools that I need.

I must build friendships along this quest. Not only with others, but the best with myself.

I must also accept life's a difficult test. Failure isn't final—it can lead to success.

Because hard work
yields great rewards,
I'll be all I can be...

Hard Work

Persistence

Self Love

Bio-mechanical Engineering

Optimism

Goal is Conquered

I'll show the whole world
what I can do.

I'm going to live my
best life too!

MARTIKA SHANEL was born in a small, rural town where the mountains were her playground. Her first ever big-girl job was exploring oil and gas platforms in the Gulf of Mexico's vast, deep, blue waters. She has lived overseas in Asia and in Europe; has the best title, mommy; and enjoys making others smile. She and her husband share a loving home with two remarkable children and enough books for a lifetime of imagination.

She aspires to encourage the youth from all backgrounds and circumstances to dream and achieve big. As a childhood victim of the opioid crisis, she hopes to instill in all students the importance of understanding that one's future is not determined by their present view of life--that they may achieve anything with the right tools: a positive mindset, a thoughtful plan, a network of mentors, and meaningful actions.

 @MartikaShanel    @MartikaShanel    @authormartikashanel

www.martikashanel.com

76542652R00020

Made in the USA
Columbia, SC
27 September 2019